Bug-Watching

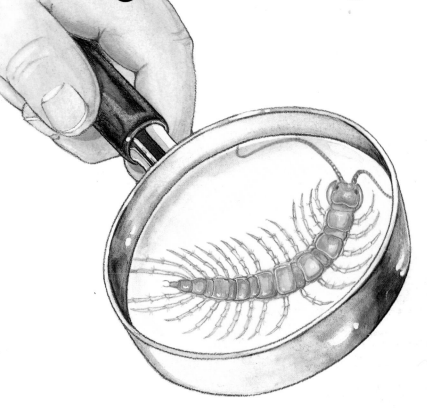

By Rebel Williams
Illustrated by Iris Nichols

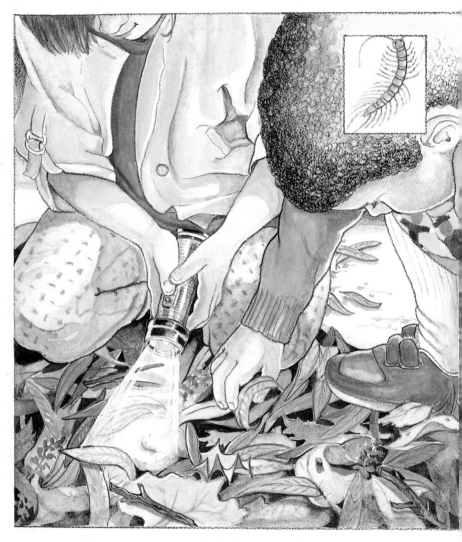

Bugs under leaves.

2

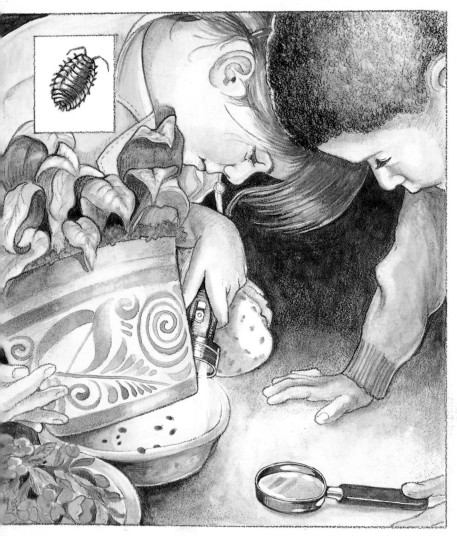

Bugs under pots.

3

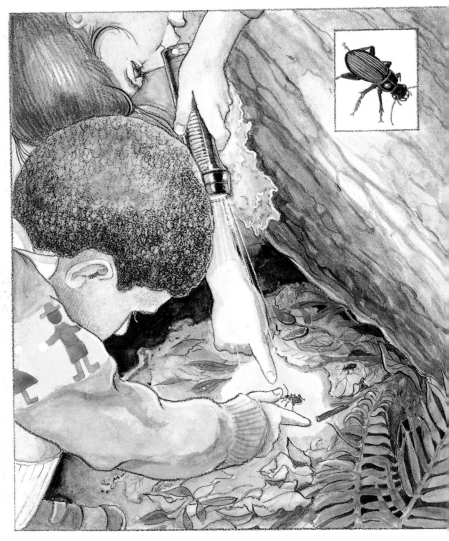

Bugs under logs.

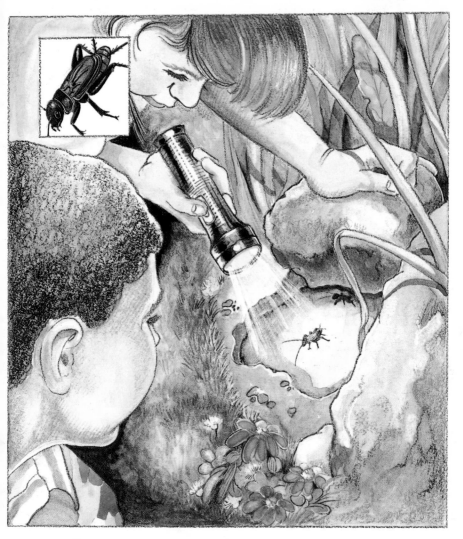

Bugs under rocks.

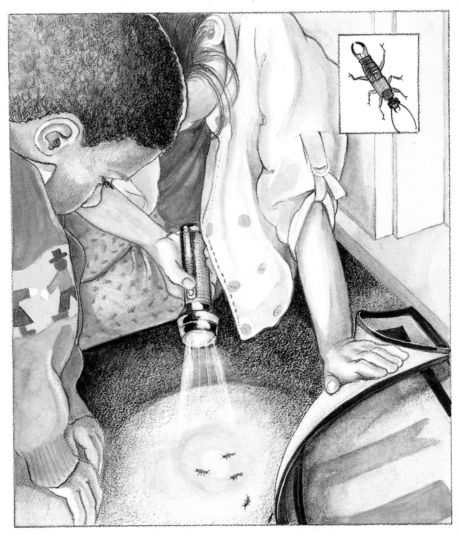

Bugs under mats.

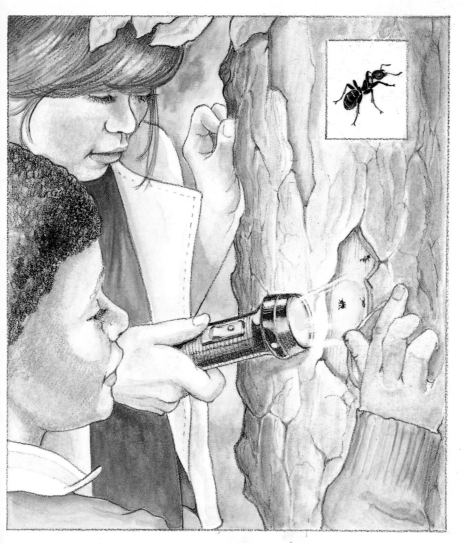

Bugs under bark.

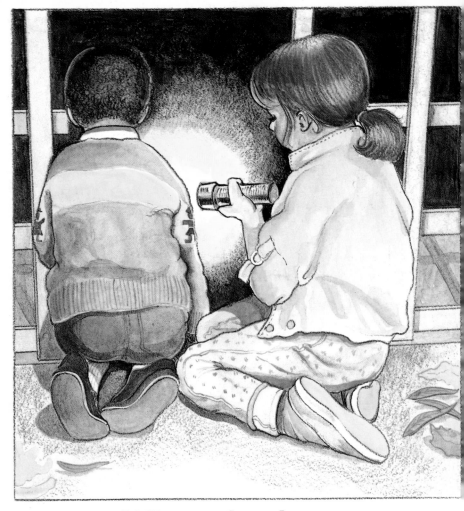

Why do bugs
live in the dark?